To get your **THREE FREE MONTHS MEMBERSHIP** to Moshi Monsters, go to **WWW.MOSHIGIFT.COM** and follow the instructions!

PUFFIN BOOKS

Published by the Penguin Group: London, New York,
Australia, Canada, India, Ireland, New Zealand and South Africa
Penguin Books Ltd, Registered Offices: 80 Strand, London WC2R 0RL, England

puffinbooks.com

First published 2014
001

Written by Andy Davidson
Illustrations by Vincent Bechet
Comic illustrations by Fran and David Brylewska

© Mind Candy Ltd. All rights reserved, 2014
All rights reserved

Made and printed in China

ISBN: 978-0-14135-389-0

British Library Cataloguing in Publication Data
A CIP catalogue record for this book is available from the British Library

CONTENTS

ALL AROUND THE WORLD

Greetings mega-Moshi fan! We're so glad you could join us on this magical trip around the whole of the Moshi world from Monstro City all the way to the jungles of Music Island. You'll learn things you didn't know and have more fun than hanging out with two dozen Cheeky Chimps.

Mrs. Snoodle's location is also your exclusive Moshi code to unlock roarsome virtual content. That's right, dear Monsters. It's enough to make you want to start a parp duet. All together now . . .

LOOKING FOR SNOODLE

Poppet, Katsuma and **Mr. Snoodle** are on the hunt for Mrs. Snoodle. She has gone missing in mysterious circumstances. You'd think she'd be easy to find with her plume of rainbow hair, but no. She's been sending them cryptic clues to find her, but where in the Moshi world could she be? **On each page that Mrs. Snoodle leaves a note you'll find a hidden letter.** Be warned, though, some of them are harder to find than the Lost Treasure of Umba Umba. It's enough to get you fizzing with frustration. Collect all the letters and unscramble them to rescue Mrs. Snoodle.

WRITE ALL OF THE LETTERS YOU FIND IN THIS HANDY BOX:

SNOODLE CLUE

Hey P, K and Mr. S, I've left you a secret letter near to each of my notes. Find all the secret letters and unscramble them to find me. The first letter is nearby!

I'm munching my way through a big bag of popcorn. See you on the silver screen.

What could it mean?

I think I know!

SUITCASE SEARCH

Some monsters pack the strangest things in their suitcases. Does anyone really need a Techies Glitchy Gazebo in their Scrambled Egg Backpack? What, you do? Well, that's just fine. OK, clever clogs, see if you can find all these items in the wordsearch.

Skull Comb
Purple Keytar
Wavy Blue Do
Ski Goggles
Flamin' Quiff
Kitty's Nose
Big Apple Hat
Gloopy Friend
Soul Shades
Eye-eeeeeeee
Mr. Roboto Mask

```
R E A U G D R F L A M I N Q U I F F X O
U G C Z D N K I T T Y S N O S E C J R F
S G K I Z E B M O C L L U K S J Q T C L
E W R O U I U M H T U V C R P U M D B Y
L T G J R R A K S A M O T O B O R R M T
G L M D I F L Q O G I G P E R K Z U W I
G N F P X Y B R O D T Y W Y Y F O B L G
O U U O L P M E E E E E E E E E Y E M S
G B Z K O O A Q J V L U H V B Z W N E H
I I W A O O S E D A H S L U O S T D Y E
K H A Z K L W V A O N Q U B M G J Y R G
S P I B I G A P P L E H A T Y K U J S A
G F C A L B S Z L D B W C N C V C K K G
D Y Y R A T Y E K E L P R U P B A A U F
L Q P S V W F I G D H V K J C V R W F N
```

PASSPORT CONTROL

Mr. Snoodle has sniffed out a clue to Mrs. Snoodle's kidnapper – Dr. Strangeglove has dropped his ID card! Strangeglove is always finding new ways to be dastardly. There's even something fishy about his ID card. Take a look at these two versions of it. There are nine differences to spot.

EVIL iD CARD

Name: DR. STRANGEGLOVE
Age: NEVER YOU MIND
Profession: EVIL GENIUS
Affiliated groups:
☠ C.L.O.N.C.

EVIL iD CARD!

Name: DR. STRANGEGLOVE
Age: NEVER YOUR MIND
Profession: EVIL GENIUS
Affiliated groups:
● C.L.O.N.C

MONSTRO CITY TRAVEL GUIDE

Buster Bumblechops, your Monstro City Travel Guide Extraordinaire here. My Moshling collecting has taken me far and wide so I'm one well-travelled Moshi. I'll be giving you inside tips on Moshi destinations that are more useful than a cake house. I mean, who doesn't want to have your cake and live in it? Ha-dee-ha. Watch out for snippets throughout your journey!

ON BOARD THE CLOUDY CLOTH CLIPPER

> Yarr! Come onto me *Cloudy Cloth Clipper*, the brownest ship to sail these seventy seas! We're headed t' a very special location, but I won't tell ye where. Ye look as brainy as Pinestein, so you'll be havin' no trouble t' find it ou' fer yerself.

MONSTRO CITY TRAVEL GUIDE

The *Cloudy Cloth Clipper* is captained by Cap'n Buck E. Barnacle with his first mate Lefty. Buck's cousin Baz runs a shop on Bleurgh Beach. Last time I was there he sold me a multicoloured hat. It was a nice hat, but the colours all ran the first time it rained. At least my beard was colourful that day.

BUCK'S HIGH SCORE

31

20

15   9

5   4

2   2

PUSH THE PUCKS

Buck loves nothing better than playing shuffleboard on a lengthy voyage, as long as his barnacle-back isn't playing up. Which four numbers would you have to land on to match the old sea dog's (not very) high score?

DESTINATION DILEMMA

Ahoy, landlubbers! Is your brain feeling ship shape? Good. As you sail along you'll pass doubloons with letters on them. Write down each in turn to find out your destination.

START

C A D N A Y O H S L S

FINISH

Island Hopping

The Moshi world is a ginormous place. What if Mrs. Snoodle is somewhere we've never even heard of?

Let's check Cap'n Buck's maps and make sure we know everywhere!

Cap'n Buck thought he had visited every island in the Seventy Seas, but you've discovered somewhere new! Draw your very own island on this piece of parchment.

MY ISLAND IS CALLED:

THEY DON'T LIKE:

THE MOSHLINGS THAT LIVE ON MY ISLAND ARE:

YOU CAN GET TO MY ISLAND BY:

THEY LIKE:

MY ISLAND IS FAMOUS FOR:

MAKE THE moshi MISSILE

Woooooooooooo! Try and beat Katusma on the Moshi Karts and you'll unleash a flurry of claws, jaws and lightning-fast moves. If you fancy a super smooth kart of your own then try making the Moshi Missile.

Don't forget to get an adult to help you! (Whatever you do don't ask a passing Fumble to help. You'll spend most of the day gluing their bits back on!)

MONSTRO CITY TRAVEL GUIDE

I'm a bit of a whizz at Moshi Karts. I once beat I.G.G.Y in a race. He was so annoyed he munched his way through my helmet. Luckily I used the Rox I earnt in the game to upgrade it. Vroom, vroom!

YOU WILL NEED:

A large plastic fabric conditioner bottle
Two large plastic deodorant lids
Two small plastic deodorant
or body spray lids
2 (clean!) coffee stirrers
2 small white plastic
yoghurt drink bottles
Black, red and white stickers
for decoration
Black sugar paper
Black and silver marker pens
Coloured pens or paints
Scissors, PVA glue and sticky tape

1 Carefully cut the top off a large conditioner bottle to make the main body of the car.

2 Cut a large hole in one side for the seat, keeping the leftover plastic. Then outline the edge with a silver marker.

10

3 Wrap a piece of black sugar paper around each of the four lids to make tyres. Use sticky tape on the insides of the two smaller lids to attach them to either end of a coffee stirrer. Repeat with the larger lids. Stick the two wheel axles onto the main body of the racing car with more tape.

4 Create two boosters out of the small yoghurt drink bottles. Use some leftover plastic from when you cut the seat hole to attach the missiles to the main body of the car.

5 Use pens or paints to create more details such as wheel arches, exhaust pipes and engine grilles. Get creative and supercharge your kart!

6 Use black and white stickers in a checkerboard pattern on the front of the car and ends of the missiles. You're done! Give yourself a monster pat on the back.

STARFISHBUCKS

STARFISHBUCKS COFFEE

Welcome to Starfishbucks – the only place to buy hot, cold and lukewarm drinks in Monstro City. Please look at the menu and tell me what you want.

I'm SO thirsty. Let's stop here for a drink.

Good idea! But why can't I read the menu?

MENU MESS-UP

Uh–oh, what have we here? It looks like those meddlesome Glumps have been at it again. Fill in the missing letters to read the menu.

S_U_ S_U_P _L_S_I_
C_R_O_ O_
S_U_ M_L_
C_P _ G_U_L
E_S_N_E O_ B_U_
T_A_ S_D_
B_G J_I_E
S_I_E R_C_E_

MONSTRO CITY TRAVEL GUIDE

 I bumped into Cali the Valley Mermaid while waiting for my cappuccino. We giggled about the time I accidentally snagged her in my net. Mind you, she was TOTALLY ticked off at the time, so I chilled her in ice, gave her a seaweed sandwich and dropped her off at the Sea Mall for a fin-icure and some retail therapy. Great tails? You betcha!

TRICKY SNACKS

Ooh, yummy, scrummy! Delicious Moshi snacks for my tummy! There should be two of each snack in the cabinet, but one got dropped on the floor. Can you work out which one?

Rumble in EAST GRUMBLE

Hey Sooki Yaki, we're having no luck tracking down Mrs. Snoodle. Can you give us some super-spy tips?

Sure thing, Poppet. Here's how to make your own spy wardrobe just like mine.

This is what you need if you want to be totally sneaky:

A pair of soft, soft shoes (for sneaking)	A black jumper (to blend in to shadows)	A backpack (to put your spy stuff in)	Sensible trousers (you can't jump over walls in anything too fancy)	Some sunglasses (to look cool)	Knitting needles and wool (to pass the time)
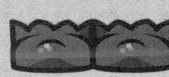					

STEALTHY CODE

I have some tippy-top secret intel on where Mrs. Snoodle has been taken. Use the Super Moshi secret code translator to decode my message. Warning: This message will disappear in thirty seconds… then reappear… then disappear again.

■⊙◇ ⦵ ⦵✕ИИ

Φ◇·❘·ⵊⵙ⊙◇❖⦵ⵙ✕⫝ , □⦂⦵

ⵊЛⴲ. ⴲ◇⊙⊙■Иⵋ ⵛ⊹ⴲ

⊙◇ Φ◇ ⵛ⊹ⴲИΦ◇■.

A	B	C	D	E	F	G
Φ	□	▽	◪	✕	ⵛ	✳

H	I	J	K	L	M	N
ⵊ	⊹	⫝	ⵙ	ⵋ	ⵚ	◇

O	P	Q	R	S	T
⊙	⌒	Ω	Л	ⴲ	ⵀ

U	V	W	X	Y	Z
⦂	⦙	✕	✳	·❘·	⦵

13

AT THE MOVIES

Roary Scrawl at your service. *Moshi Monsters: The Movie* was the greatest film to hit the cinemas ever! I couldn't take any of my eyes off it.

ON LOCATION

Wow, this was one of my favourite bits! I needed eyes in the back of my head to take in all the action that was going on. **Can you spot eight differences between the two movie stills?**

PROPS DEPARTMENT

Don't freak, but the props department made the mistake of lending Zommer some stuff used in the movie and it has all come back with pieces missing. Can you spot which parts are missing on the following items?

A   B   C

E   F   G

MOVIE POSTER

There's panic in the marketing department. A Tickly Pickle has sneezed clouds of itching powder all over the place and everymoshi's too busy scratching to do their jobs. They need a movie poster designed and fast. Help them out for Moshi's sake.

SNOODLE CLUE

Look around this area. Wherever you find one of my notes, you'll find a letter. Find all the letters to find out where I am!

The next location is filled with hundreds of tiny flapping wings.

Tiny wings?

I have an idea!

MAIN STREET MAYHEM

Shopping is meant to be relaxing, but someone should really tell that to Main Street! Hustle, bustle, monsters and trouble. It's here you'll find Snozzle Wobbleson's Gross-ery Store, the headquarters of the *Daily Growl* or you can pick up something strangely delightful from the Bizarre Bazaar.

UNDER CONSTRUCTION

There's a new shop opening on Main Street and you've got to design it. The sky's the limit, so really put your creative power to use. Ready, set, gooool!

GROSS ERY

MOSHLING SEEDS

MONSTRO CITY TRAVEL GUIDE

I was feeling a bit peckish last time I was strolling down Main Street. Lucky for me I bumped into Micro Dave, the Popty-Ping. He heated me up some Gloop Soup before I could say Toffee Crunch Couch. Just don't try to pick him up and pop him in your pocket – those oven mitts get really hot! Ouch!

sigh Main Street's always busy.

Don't worry, I know a shortcut through.

Fill in the names of the Moshi items on this shopping list. The first letters of each item will reveal something extra to buy!

EXTRA ITEM:

Toad Soda

Green

Eye Pie

Spamburger

Pumpkin Pie

Mice Krispies

Roast Beast

Slop

Snail Ale

Bangers and Mash

A Sauce of Course

Mr. Tea

BABS' BOUTIQUE

Oh dear. Someone just mistook an Oakey-Doke Hokey Poke for a seat and now everything in the boutique is covered with slippy sap. Help Babs restock, fast, by drawing in some new products she can sell. Here's a handy list of items you could use.

BINGO BONGO DRUMS
BOWLER BALLS
MONSTER BABY PHOTOS
GUMMY BEAR LAMP
FRIED EGG RUG
A NEW WALLPAPER

Moshling Zoo

Tamara Tesla here, Monstro City's very own brainiac scientist. The Moshi world is packed full of Moshlings. There are so many of them even I sometimes lose count!

MONSTRO CITY TRAVEL GUIDE

Ah, there's nothing more exciting than a trip to a Moshling Zoo. Although herding up the little critters and trying to convince them to stay can be tricky. I remember the time I had to chase Marty the Mouthy Mogul across the Moshi Movie set. Or did he chase me? I can't quite remember. Every time you complete a set of Moshlings, that set gets a special background. Another reason to find as many Moshlings as possible!

Reckon you're a Moshling mastermind?

You're going to need all the brainpower you have to complete this Moshing mind boggler. Use your masterful Moshi knowledge to tackle these eight tough questions. Take the first letter of each answer to make an anagram of one of the Moshlings below. Which one could it be?

Write the first letter for each answer in these boxes:

Now unscramble the Moshling's name and write it in this box!

1. You'll find this five-pointed Moshling working at Starfishbucks.

2. Call for this robotic Moshling when you need to reach something high up.

3. Otherwise known as a Cranky Codfather.

4. The most circular Moshling.

5. This Moshling is native to Meringue Meadow.

6. The only one of the Ponies that can fly.

7. A nutty Woodland Walnut.

8. An actual cat burglar.

18

FROSTY POP GLACIER

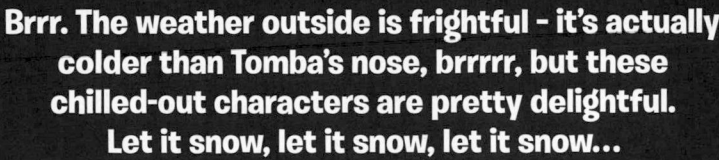

Brrr. The weather outside is frightful - it's actually colder than Tomba's nose, brrrrr, but these chilled-out characters are pretty delightful. Let it snow, let it snow, let it snow...

We've got winter chills – they're electrifyin'!

PEPPY

Peppy the Stunt Penguin loves living on the Frosty Pop Glacier. The icy conditions are perfect for doing skids on his bike and for scoffing pilchard popsicles. Yuckity yuck.

THE FREEZY RIDERS

These ice-cool Stunt Penguins are the very best Moshlings on two wheels – not easy when your mitts are frozen – and especially when their feet don't even touch the pedals. When lost they can usually be found at the nearest fridge.

GRACIE

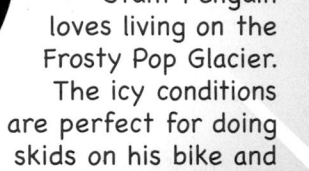

There are no Moshlings more swishy than a Swishy Missy, that's a FACT. They're not so swishy off the ice, though. Maybe 'cos they refuse to remove their magical ice skates.

TOMBA

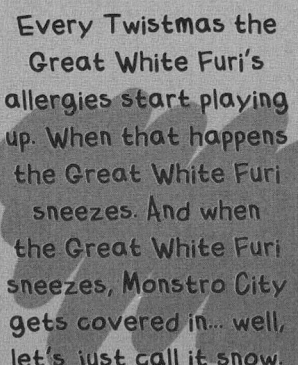

Feeling chilly? There must be a Wistful Snowtot nearby because these frosty little Moshlings are made of ice, snow and stuff we don't know. As their name suggests, they're usually glum – hardly surprising when abominable critters are always kicking them to bits. Worse still, they can only smell carrots. Heartbrrr-eaking.

MONSTRO CITY TRAVEL GUIDE

The Moshi Frosty Games is the most goodpendous gala of games in history. It's Moshi vs Moshi on games like Bug Rush, Beanstalk Bounce and Thump-a-Glump. Every monster wants Elder Furi's ultimate prize - the monsterific ice sculpture. No need to worry about keeping it inside. When the ice melts, a little Moshi magic has it looking as good as new in two shakes of a Frazzledragon's tail.

THE GREAT WHITE FURI

Every Twistmas the Great White Furi's allergies start playing up. When that happens the Great White Furi sneezes. And when the Great White Furi sneezes, Monstro City gets covered in... well, let's just call it snow.

Wow your friends with this optical illusion, puzzle peeps. Which of these Great White Furi footprints is biggest? Only the smartest Moshis will suss it.

FLUTTERBY FIELD

Flutterby Field is packed with Flutterbies. If you're the pits at catching the little flappers, why not make one instead?

YOU WILL NEED:

A piece of square paper
Two thin strips of paper for antennae
Glue
Pens or paper

ORIGAMI FLUTTERBY

1 Fold the piece of paper in half to make a triangle.

2 Fold this triangle in half again.

3 Now fold the edge of each triangle down separately at the angle shown in the picture.

4 Unfold the triangle to leave a butterfly shape. Press the centre to make the wings flap.

5 Glue the strips of paper on as antennae and decorate your Flutterby with pens or paints. Isn't it BEEEEEAUTIFUL?

SNOODLE CLUE

Have you found the next letter?

Once you have, look for somewhere hot and filled with cuddly cubs!

This one's easy!

It is?

20

CANDY CANE CAVES

Welcome to the cupcakiest caves in the whole Moshi world. These decadent caverns are crammed full of cakes, cakes and more cakes!

EASY PEASY SQUEEZY CUPCAKES!

Fancy whipping up some tasty Moshi-style cupcakes of your own? Of course you do! Try this sugary paradise of a recipe. You never know which Moshling will love your yummy cupcake in their tummy.

Remember, always get an adult to help you when using the oven. (Whatever you do check there are no Amazin' Blazin' Raisins anywhere around. Unless you want your cupcakes to go up in flames. Twisted firestarters? You bet.)

- [x] Preheat the oven to 180C/350F/Gas 4 and line a twelve-hole muffin tin with paper cases.

- [x] Cream the butter and sugar together in a bowl until pale. Beat in the eggs a little at a time then stir in the vanilla extract.

- [ ] Fold in the flour using a large metal spoon, and add in the milk.

- [ ] Spoon the mixture into the paper cases until they are half full.

- [x] Bake in the oven for fifteen minutes, until golden-brown on top.

- [x] Carefully remove from tin and cool on a wire rack.

- [ ] To make the icing, beat the butter in a large bowl until soft. Add half the icing sugar and beat until smooth.

- [ ] Add the remaining icing sugar with the milk, beat until smooth and creamy.

- [ ] Add the food colouring and mix until well combined.

- [x] Use a spoon or a piping bag to swirl the icing on to the top of the cakes.

- [x] Top with sweets or cake decorations. See if you can beat the Swirl-berry Muffin – the winner of the Tallest Swirl of the Year award.

YOU WILL NEED:

CAKE
110g/4oz butter or margarine, softened at room temperature
110g/4oz caster sugar
2 free-range eggs, beaten
1 tsp vanilla extract
110g/4oz self-raising Flour
1 tbsp milk

ICING
140g/5oz butter, softened
280g/10oz icing sugar
1 tbsp milk
A few drops of food colouring of your choice
A selection of sweets or cake decorations

MONSTRO CITY TRAVEL GUIDE

Ever wondered what the Roarkers are doing in the Candy Cane Caves? They're drilling for syrup. They sell it by the barrelful to Snozzle Wobbleson. Moshlings love cupcakes. You might even be able to tempt a Mollycoddled Manamana away from its cosy rock cavern with one of these delicious dainties.

BLEUGH BEACH

Bleurgh Beach is packed no matter what time of year it is. Moshlings and monsters come here to enjoy the sea breeze, play in the salty Potion Ocean and build sandcastles.

We've gotta get to the other side of the beach.

Not before I get my souvenirs! Can you give me a paw?

Give Katsuma a paw finding all these souvenirs!

Three Ice Screams
Two Golden Crabs
Five sandcastles
A surfboard
A pair of sun glasses
Four Cuddly Humans

VOLCANO FIASCO

Shhh. The volcano is where the Super Moshis have their secret headquarters. Blocking anyone from entering is the Gatekeeper. This key-loving guardian has no body with him - literally, because he's just a head. Get past him if you can!

357

179   **191**

100   **91**

48   **52**

21   **26**

12

7   **5**   **5**   **7**   **5**

3   **2**

1   **2**   **2**   **1**   **2**   **1**   **1**   **2**   **2**   **1**   **1**

As the Gatekeeper of the Super Moshi HQ, I cannot let anymoshi pass unless they can solve this befuddling braintwister.

Each box on the volcano contains a number, which is the total of the two numbers below it. Fill in the missing numbers to open the volcano. It's enough to get your brain into a lava…

SUPER MOSHI SEARCH

Your mission is to find all these words hidden in the grid. It's tougher than a bag of hammers!

Super	Luvli	Elder Furi	Strangeglove
Moshi	Furi	C.L.O.N.C.	Tamara Tesla
Poppet	Diavlo	Glumps	Bumblechops
Katsuma	Zommer	Zoshlings	Sweet Tooth

SUPER-SECRET SUPER HQ

Hey! How did you get in here? Well, now you're here you may as well get to work. Have a go at this fiendishly epic word search and fill out your Super Moshi identity card.

```
M G S P O H C E L B M U B V E
L B E E W B A M U S T A K R L
E F V Y J K N R T T U X E A D
V S P M U L G B L R T X P L E
D I A V L O M L D A F G M E R
K M N Z A E Z A M N D V H I F
C R E P U S G A Z G I P T H U
A Z O M M E R O B E C X O S R
Y S A Y C A S Q A G W P O O I
M D H N T H Z U I L Q P T M D
F I O E L L F Z R O O O T D Y
U L S I U Y E R U V C P E B V
C L N V L R W S F E I P E I Y
A G L Y T I S H M K P E W B K
S I B D K J H J M N K T S F J
```

OFFICIAL SM ID CARD

Super Moshi name: _____

Secret identity: _____

Super powers: _____

Biggest enemy: _____

Super-best friend: _____

Super Moshlings sidekick: _____

 SM I solemnly swear to fight for right and to uphold the Heroes' Code. ✓

SUPER MOSHI ID

Look up in the sky! Is it a Birdie? Is it the C.L.O.N.C. Blimp? No, it's YOU – a brand spanking new Super Moshi. Congratulations! Fill in this identity card, photocopy it and remember to keep it on you at all times.

24

THE UNDERGROUND DISCO

If you make it past Bubba the Bouncer you'll find yourself in Monstro City's most exclusive nightspot, the Underground Disco. You can rub shoulders with Zack Binspin, Simon Growl, Tyra Fangs, Hoolio, Ziggy and loads more gooperstars. So put on your colourful legwarmers, shimmy into your disco pants and get ready to bust some Moshi moves to the latest bad beats.

Learn these easy peasy gooberry squeezy dance steps and you can get funky the next time you're listening to the coolest tracks on the block on the Moshi Monsters Music app.

1. Stand with your feet slightly apart and arms by your sides.

2. Nod your head three times in time with the beat.

3. Raise your left arm straight up.

4. Now raise your right arm up to meet it.

5. Put your arms back down by your sides and step once to your left.

6. Now jump back to the right and clap your hands.

7. Crouch down to the floor and wait for two seconds.

8. Then jump up with your hand raised.

MONSTRO CITY TRAVEL GUIDE

When I'm not strutting my stuff being a total heartthrob on stage, I just love playing my top tunes on the Moshi Music app. I can check out all the latest tunes from Bingo, I.G.G.Y. and Pooky – but my favourite musical masterpiece? My very own 'Head Over Heels' of course.

Quack!

Woo-hoo. That's it, you're doing the Moshi Boogie!

STASHLEY'S ON THE CASE!

Ahh, another quiet day in Monstro City.

Hurnk! Graffiti? Not on my watch. I'd better look for clues.

the graffiti guru woz 'ere

No one's better at finding graffiti than me!

GASP! That's me!

you'll never catch me! -the graffiti guru

See you at the docks

I know you're out there guru.

Ah-ha! A clue. I'll dash to the docks and catch the graffiti guru red-handed.

GAH! The guru!

JOLLYWOOD

Do you feel like you're being followed by a rainy Dinky Dreamcloud? Are you down in the Glumps? Then you must be in need of a trip to Jollywood! One thing is guaranteed, visit here and you'll come away feeling jolly good.

Bobbi SingSong

Jollywood's most famous resident Moshling is that master of mantras, Bobbi SingSong. This Jollywood Singaling is a true gooperstar – he's been known to hang out at the Sandy Drain Hotel with Zac Binspin and Simon Growl!

WRITER'S BLOCK

Bobbi has nearly finished writing a follow-up to his ultra-smash mega-hit 'Welcome to Jollywood'. Unfortunately, writer's block has struck and he just can't finish off the last line. It's up to you to finish the lyrics.

WELCOME TO JOLLYWOOD

Get down to the Jollywood beat, Stand on your head and wave your feet. If you're a monster let me hear you say,

_____

_____

LIGHTS, CAMERAS, MOSHI!

Not only is Jollywood well known for its groovy singers, red-hot spices and Blue Snuggly Tiger Cubs, it's also home to the fabulous Moshi TV Studios. This is where Moshi fans from all over the world can upload their very own Moshi videos.

Moshi TV STUDIOS

MOE PUKKA

Does Moe Pukka remind you of anyone? That's 'cos he's related to Monstro City's very own Moe Yukky.

The two faces of Moe Pukka

Normally Moe looks like this.

But when he eats something really spicy he looks like this!

BIG CHIEF TINY HEAD

Look out, there's a C.L.O.N.C.ster about! Big Chief Tiny Head has been known to hang around Jollywood trying to find his way back to his former big-headed glory. If you see him, just chuck some BongoColada juice his way, he can't resist the stuff!

Big Chief Tiny Head wants an image change. Draw a new headdress for his tiny noggin

29

BARMY SWAMI JUNGLE HUNT

Deep in the lush green Barmy Swami Jungle the Snuggly Tiger Cubs live. Take a careful look at this page and see if you can spot the ten cubs sharpening their claws. Be warned, it's harder to crack than a rusty swoonafish can.

A Blue Snuggly Tiger Cub is taking the weight off his paws while on holiday from Jollywood. See if you can spot him.

SNOODLE CLUE

Don't forget to find the hidden letter.

Where am I next? Here's a clue: baby Moshlings!

I'm guessing you know the answer to this one?

Yep!

30

DRESS UP POPPET

Hello, Poppet here. Calling all my creative fans, it's time to pump up the glam. I totally heart trying out new looks. This is your chance to style me exactly the way you want to. Glam, sassy, kooky or classy, it's up to you. C'mon, strike a pose!

Unless you want your annual to look like a Musky Husky mistook it for a doggy bag, photocopy these pages and cut the copies out instead!

Simply cut out and slot in place.

DRESS UP POPPET

Simply cut out and slot in place.

DRESS UP KATSUMA

Simply cut out and slot in place.

I <3 Moshlings

Hello, Poppet here! I just adore Moshlings and if you like squeezably huggable Moshlings as much as me then you've come to the right page. Check it out!

MEGA MOSHLING MINI QUIZ

1. Which Moshling is sometimes explosive?

2. What brainy Moshling do you get if you cross a tropical fruit with a nutty professor?

3. Which rebellious Moshling could help you do some graffiti?

4. Which wiggly way-cool Moshling can't resist making jazzy sounds 24/7 by poking out his tongue and shaking his jellybean tail rattle?

5. Which musical Brassy Blowything enjoys burping rainbow-coloured bubbles whenever he marches in time to their toot-tastic ditties?

MY MOSHLING NAME

What's in a name? Well, there's only one way to find out. Find the first letter of your first name in the left box, then the first letter of your second name in the box on the right. Put the two words together to make your Moshling name!

Arty	Nosey	Ankle	Nut
Breezy	Orange	Boom-boom	Oat
Chalky	Pencil	Cat	Pipkin
Dynamo	Queen	Digger	Quiche
Egg	Rink	Elbows	Rat
Fluffy	Squishy	Furlong	Smoochy
Grunty	Trouser	Groat	Throstle
Harold	Umbrella	Hummer	Uncle
Igloo	Vanilla	Inky	Vapour
Jumping	Whistles	Jasper	Winch
King	X-Ray	Kerb	Xavier
Lemon	Yamabama	Little	Yukea
Missus	Zebra	Money	Zoo

Blingo!

SNOODLE CLUE

Keep your eyes peeled for the missing letter.

I've given my captor the slip long enough to catch up with my Flashy Fox Friend.

My Moshling name is: _____

Poppets®
TRAVEL JOURNAL

Oh no, Poppet's come down with Gombala Gombala Jungle Fever. (The poor little critter still manages to look huggaliciously cute even with a monstrous fever of 104°F and a Slug Slurp Slushie ice-pack on her head.) While she recovers, help her out by carrying on her journal.

JOLLYWOOD

Fangtastic

Cutie

Amaze

Goopendous

OMM!

Day 40

Katsuma and I are getting closer on our quest to find Mrs. Snoodle. Yesterday, we found pumpernickel breadcrumbs heading towards Gift Island. We started following them when we were suddenly stopped by . . .

Monstrous

GAMES STARCADE

Hey, I'm Raarghly and this is my shop, the Games Starcade. Want some games in your monster's room? I've got 'em. Six armfuls of them, in fact. Feel free to test out the games and share any space food you've got on you.

BUG's BIG BOUNCE

These Four Moshlings have decided that they want to bounce around just like Bug. Can you tell who they are?

SEA MONSTER MUNCH

These Sea Monsters have been busy chowing down on fish. Which of the three has grown the longest?

A

B

C

OCTO'S ECO ADVENTURE

Octo's in trouble, just look at all that trash. Help her out by counting up the number of bin bags that are on the screen. You might even get a spray for your trouble.

THE BADDIELAC 9000

Here it is - a rare sighting of Dr. Strangeglove's famous ride, the Baddielac 9000. (It's usually just a purple blur whizzing by.) The Sinister Minister likes to drive this C.L.O.N.C.tastic car around Monstro City, belching out stinky exhaust fumes and leaving tyre marks on Ooh La Lane!

FIRE-BREATHING GLOOP SPREADER

TERRIBLE TAILFINS
Purely for show, but they look REALLY mean.

SELF-DESTRUCT-O-MATIC
Causes the Baddielac 9000 to explode into goo-splattered bits.

GOO BOOSTER

DELUXE EAR WHACKER 2078 SOUND SYSTEM
Blasts out scary organ music.

BOINGTASTIC EJECTOR SEAT
Boings Dr. Strangeglove speedily out of harm's way.

HIDDEN GLUMP-BLASTERS

C.L.O.N.C.-TASTIC EXTENDABLE HUBCAPS

POWER BULGE

QUAD-ATOMIC-G INJECTED JET ENGINE

C.L.O.N.C. ENGINEERS

Help make the Baddielac dream machine go even faster by designing a super-powered rocket booster crazy contraption in this space.

I ♥ EVIL

GOOGENHEIM GALLERY GAZING

Thank you for visiting Monstro City's most intellectual attraction. Please be silent while viewing the art and refrain from taking any photographs.

ART ZOSHLINGS

One of the Zoshling's quirky paintings is going up in the gallery. Read the description and then decide which one it is.

'The first thing that caught my eye was the artist's use of the colour pink. The avant gard-ist use of alien tentacles rather than brushstrokes really makes this piece of art stand out, almost as much as this Zoshling's eyes stick out of his head!'

CAPTAIN SQUIRK

DR. C. FINGZ

SPLUTNIK

FIRST OFFICER OOZE

SO MANY SQUARES

How many squares can you count in this piece of Moshi modern art? Write your answer in the box.

Number of squares: ☐

FUNNY FORGERY

Bristly brush-offs! Mustachio has swapped one of these statues for a forgery! Can you spot it?

The forged one is: ☐

MISSING PIECE

This painting is incomplete. (We think. It's hard to tell.) Which of these pieces will finish it off?

HALF DONE

Zzzzz. This Artful Splodger got bored and only half finished this painting of a famous monster. Help out by finishing it!

A

B

C

D

EMPTY CANVAS

There's still room in the wibbly-wobbly gallery for more art. Draw your own masterpiece here and send it in to the Googenheim!

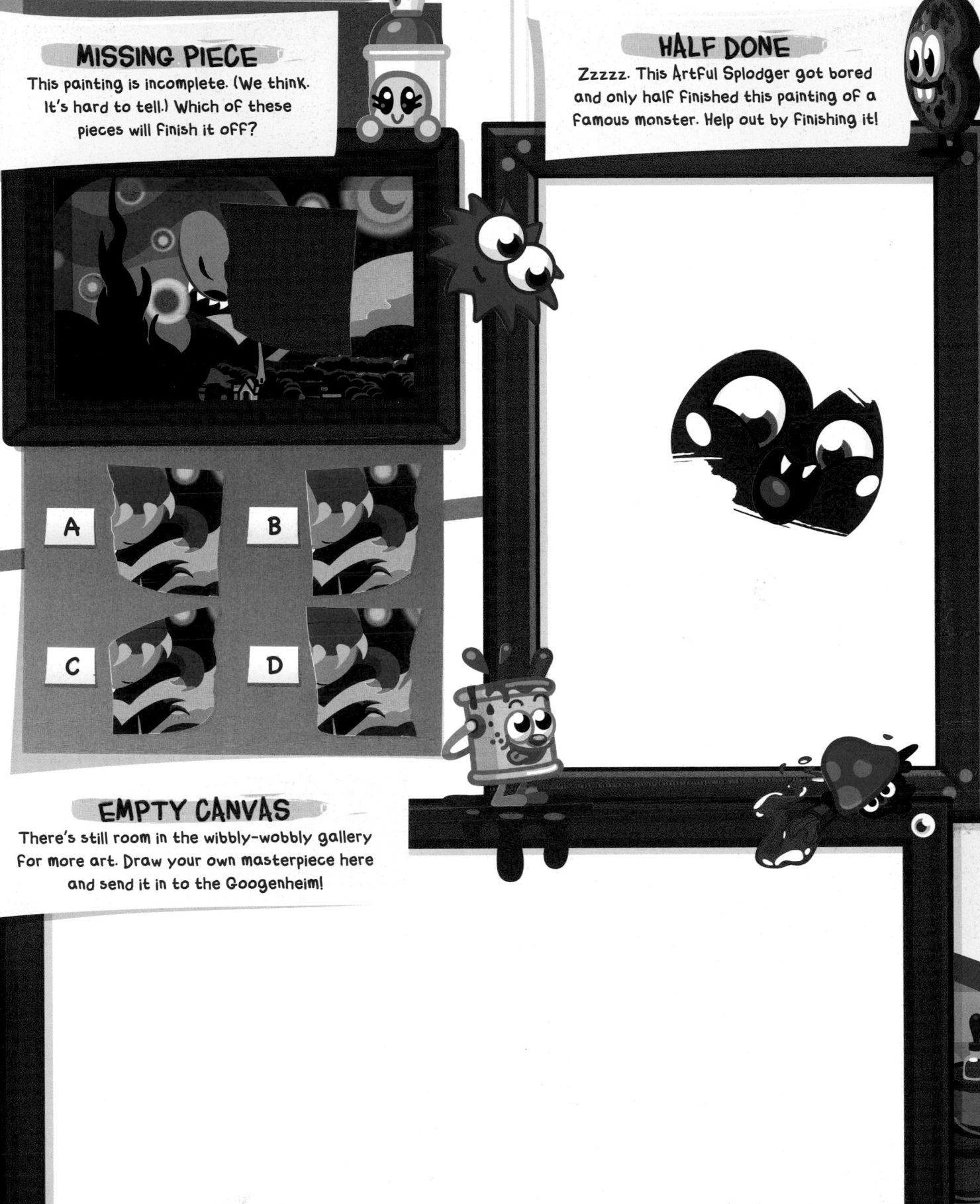

KATSUMA UNLEASHED

Sharpen your claws and get ready to defeat the evil Robot Moshlings. Bash your way through this mind-melting monsterific maze. What are you waiting for? Let the fur fly!

START

WORLD 1

WORLD 2

WORLD 4

WORLD 3

WORLD 6

WORLD 5

FINISH

HONG BONG ISLAND

MOSHI FACT

Well whaddya know, trivia fans? Shopkeeper Wobbleson is related to Monstro City's very own Snozzle Wobbleson.

The currency on Hong Bong Island is the Gold Coin. Rox are not accepted here.

KRAZY KITTENS

One of these Kittens of Good Fortune is not so lucky, lucky, lucky. Can you spot which?

A B C D

E F G H

NOODLE TRAIL

One of Suey's gooey-chewy noodles has stuck to this pile of Gold Coins. Which noodle is it?

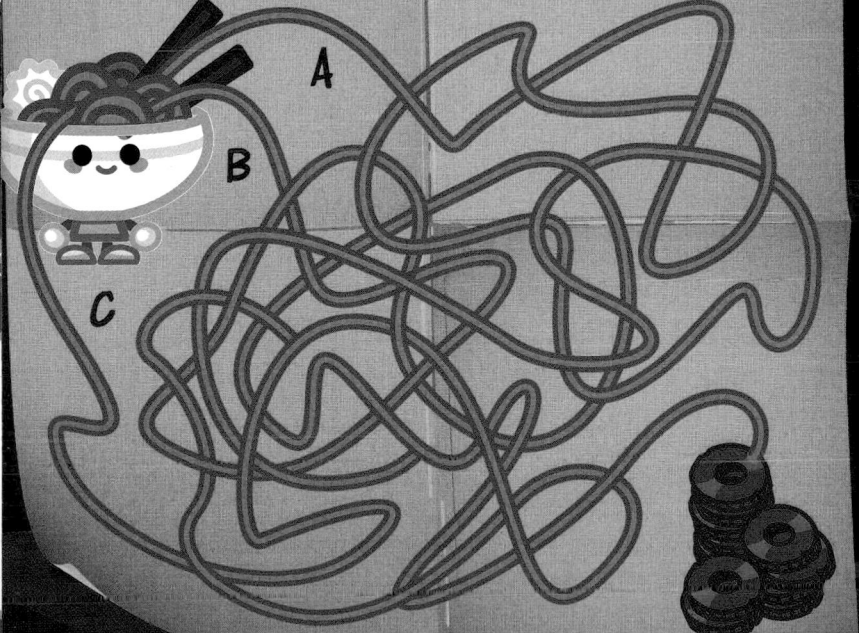

A

B

C

SILLY SILHOUETTES

Presenting the most exclusive and exciting items for sale on Hong Bong Island. If you can guess which is which, you can buy them!

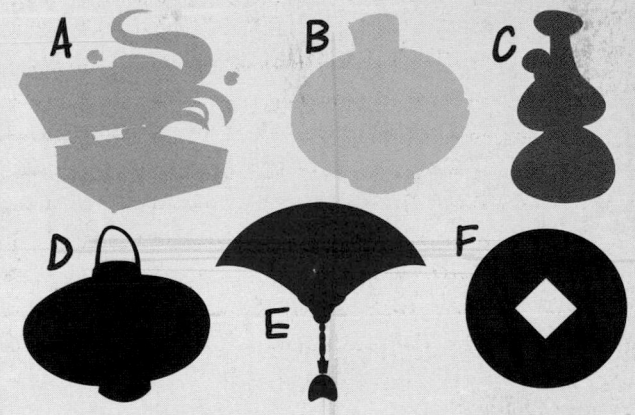

A   B   C

D   E   F

1. Hong Bong Box of Destiny
2. Tangerine Dream Lantern
3. Coin of Enchantment
4. Hong Bong Bluey Lantern
5. Flashing Fan of Fancy
6. Dingaling Decanter

43

Gift Island

Scrumpy's a specialist at all things surreal, and they don't come much more surreal than this muddled up Gift Island poster. Give the little snooper a hand solving this mystery by rearranging the pieces so they fit together.

MONSTRO CITY TRAVEL GUIDE

Gift Island is the place to go if you want to send a pal a gift. Go on, it's far better to gift than to receive!

You could send me a gift, no one ever thinks of poor Buster, *sniff*.

Unless you want your annual to look like a Picarrgghhso gone very wrong indeed, photocopy this page and cut the copy out instead!

POSTCARD SHOP

TO THE PORT →

GIFT SHOP

MONSTA-GRAMS

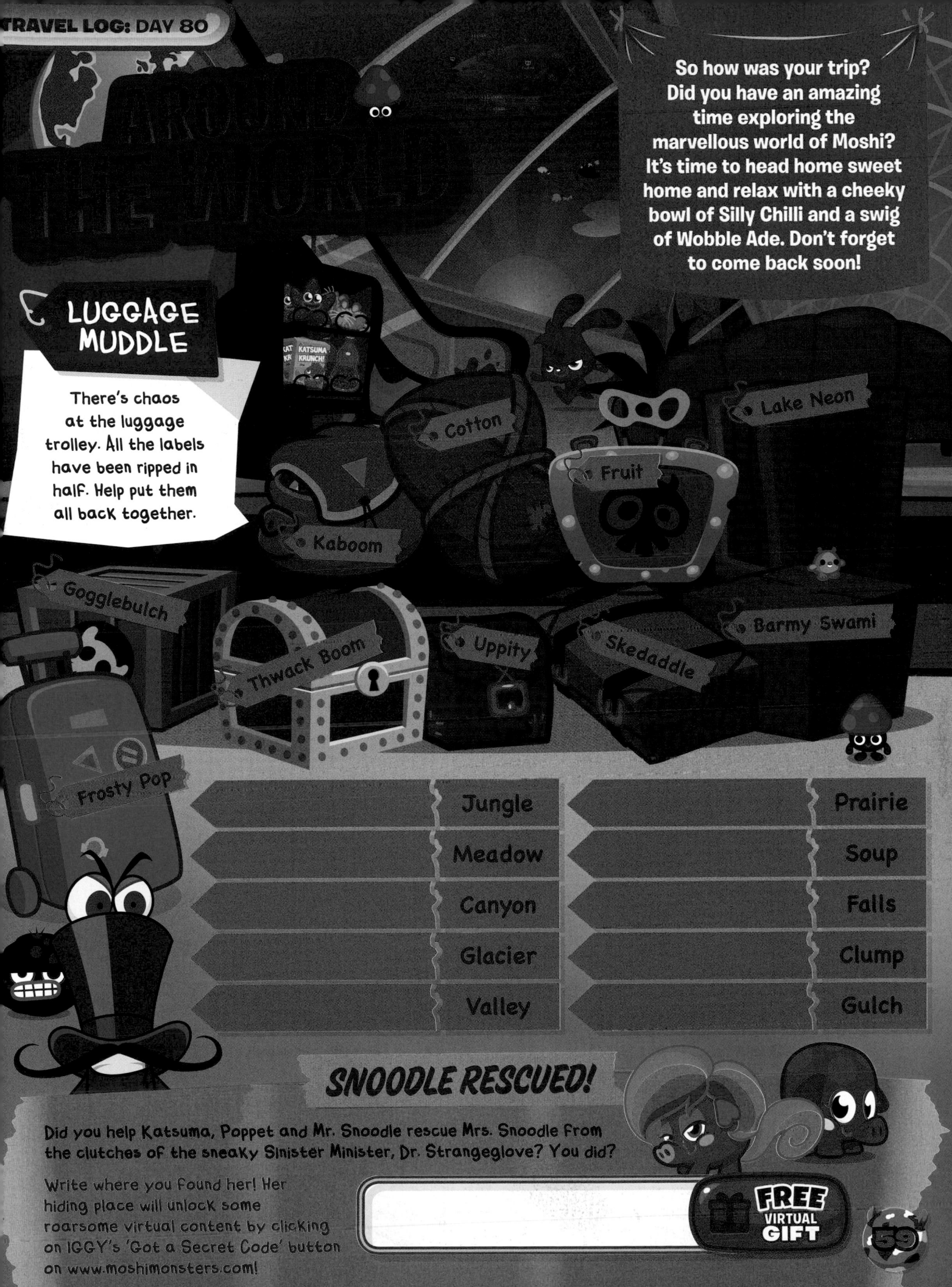

AROUND THE WORLD

So how was your trip? Did you have an amazing time exploring the marvellous world of Moshi? It's time to head home sweet home and relax with a cheeky bowl of Silly Chilli and a swig of Wobble Ade. Don't forget to come back soon!

LUGGAGE MUDDLE

There's chaos at the luggage trolley. All the labels have been ripped in half. Help put them all back together.

Cotton

Fruit

Lake Neon

Kaboom

Gogglebulch

Thwack Boom

Uppity

Skedaddle

Barmy Swami

Frosty Pop

	Jungle		Prairie
	Meadow		Soup
	Canyon		Falls
	Glacier		Clump
	Valley		Gulch

SNOODLE RESCUED!

Did you help Katsuma, Poppet and Mr. Snoodle rescue Mrs. Snoodle from the clutches of the sneaky Sinister Minister, Dr. Strangeglove? You did?

Write where you found her! Her hiding place will unlock some roarsome virtual content by clicking on IGGY's 'Got a Secret Code' button on www.moshimonsters.com!

FREE VIRTUAL GIFT

ANSWERS

PAGE 7

PASSPORT CONTROL

EVIL ID CARD!!
Name: DR. STRANGEGLOVE
Age: NEVER YOUR MIND
Profession: EVIL GENIUS
Affiliated groups:
C.L.O.N.C.

SUITCASE SEARCH >

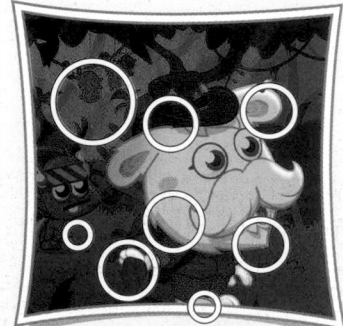

PAGE 8

DESTINATION DILEMMA

START
FINISH

PUSH PUCKS > 15, 9, 5, 2

Destination: CANDY SHOALS

PAGE 12

STARFISHBUCKS Slug Slurp Slushie, Carton Of Sour Milk, Cup O Gruel, Essence Of Blue, Toad Soda, Bug Juice, Slime Rickey

TRICKY SNACKS Missing item:

PAGE 13

STEALTHY CODE
Don't tell anymonster, but Mrs Snoodle is on an island

PAGE 19

THE GREAT WHITE FURI
Both footprints are the same.

PAGES 14-15

ON LOCATION

PROPS DEPARTMENT
A. Ship
B. Strings
C. Poppet
D. Paintbrush
E. Eyes
F. Pearl

PAGES 16-17

SHOPPING LIST CODE
Mice Krispies
Roast Beast
Toad Soda
Eye Pie
A Sauce Of Course

Extra item:
Mr. Tea

PAGE 18

1. Fumbles
2. Nipper
3. Uncle Scallops
4. Oddie
5. Dipsy
6. Angel
7. Nutmeg
8. Raffles

Hidden Moshling:
Furnando

PAGE 22

BLURGH BEACH

PAGE 30

BARMY SWAMI JUNGLE HUNT

PAGE 23

VOLCANO FIASCO

		371	357	369		
	192	179	178	191		
100	92	87	91	100		
52	48	44	43	48	52	
27	25	23	21	22	26	26
14	13	12	11	10	12	14	12
7	7	6	6	5	5	7	5
3	4	3	3	2	3	4	3	2
1	2	2	1	1	1	2	2	1	1

PAGE 24

SUPER MOSHI SEARCH

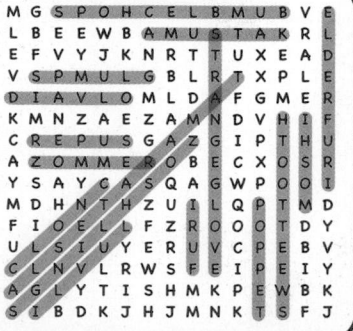

PAGE 35

MOSHLING QUIZ
1. Cherry Bomb 2. Pinestein
3. Misty 4. Hissy 5. Oompah

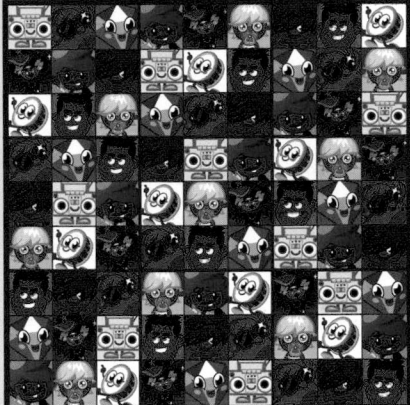
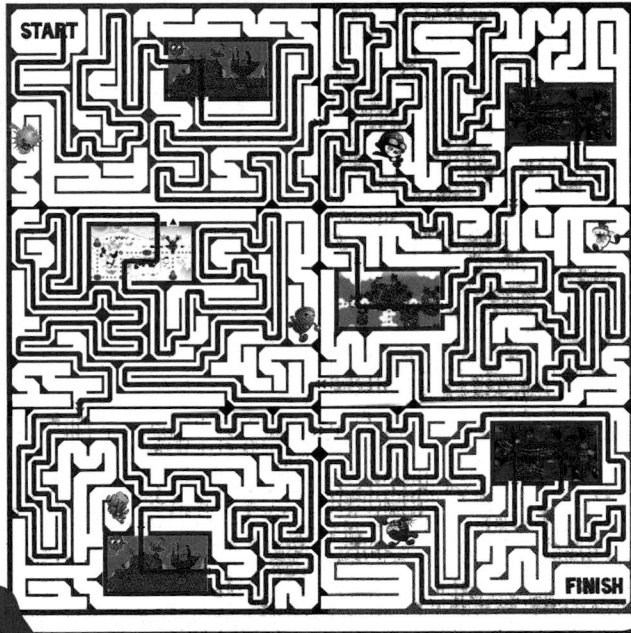